The Town
Turtles
of Sandy Springs

This book is dedicated to the imagination of children.

May it always be encouraged.

The Town Turtles of Sandy Springs

The Stories
Behind
The Turtles
by
The Children
Who Saw Them

Edited by
Martin Moran, M.D.

Hardin Publishing, LLC
Atlanta

Printed in the United States of America

For information, Hardin Publishing, LLC,
1380 West Paces Ferry Road, NW
Atlanta, Georgia, 30327
www.hardinpublishing.com

ISBN 0-9742704-1-5

Design and Layout by Esther Patrick, Atlanta, Georgia.

First Hardcover Edition

10 9 8 7 6 5 4 3 2 1

Sandy Springs

Sandy Springs is a city on the north side of Atlanta, Georgia. In 2005 the state legislature, after repeated requests over many years, allowed the community to become a city. The city of Sandy Springs has 85,000 citizens.

The land of Sandy Springs was under the control of the Creek Indians until 1821 when the land was given to the state of Georgia and placed in Henry County. Late in 1821, the land was switched to Fayette County. The next year it became part of DeKalb County. Finally, Fulton County was formed in 1853. This is where Sandy Springs continues to be located. If a boy or girl had lived in Sandy Springs from January, 1821, to December, 1853, he or she would have lived under the control of the Creek Indians and then four different Georgia counties all without moving.

The Town Turtles of Sandy Springs is a project of the Sandy Springs Society, with Northside Hospital as the presenting sponsor. The Sandy Springs Society is a philanthropic organization which raises money for local charities. Seventy-five turtles were sponsored by individuals, foundations, and businesses, painted by local artists, and then sold in September, 2005, with all of the profits going to charity. Before being sold, the turtles were placed throughout the city and enjoyed by thousands of people.

This book contains pictures of some of the turtles together with stories children have written about their favorite turtle.

I hope you enjoy the turtle stories as much as I have. By the way, this book has pictures of six turtles from Sandy Springs who don't have a story about them. I hope you will write your own story about those turtles or draw pictures of them.

Enjoy,
Martin Moran, M. D.

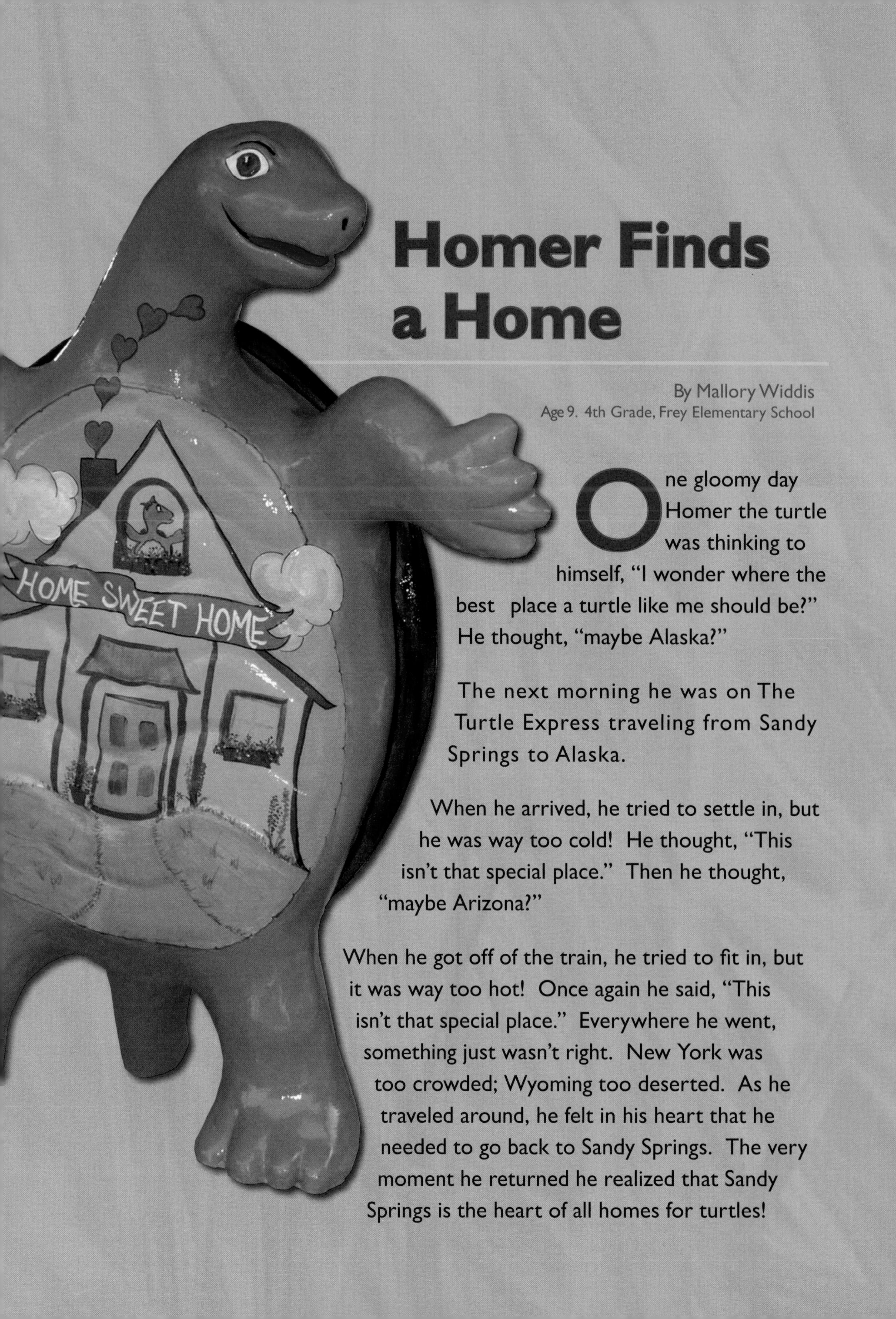

Homer Finds a Home

By Mallory Widdis
Age 9. 4th Grade, Frey Elementary School

One gloomy day Homer the turtle was thinking to himself, "I wonder where the best place a turtle like me should be?" He thought, "maybe Alaska?"

The next morning he was on The Turtle Express traveling from Sandy Springs to Alaska.

When he arrived, he tried to settle in, but he was way too cold! He thought, "This isn't that special place." Then he thought, "maybe Arizona?"

When he got off of the train, he tried to fit in, but it was way too hot! Once again he said, "This isn't that special place." Everywhere he went, something just wasn't right. New York was too crowded; Wyoming too deserted. As he traveled around, he felt in his heart that he needed to go back to Sandy Springs. The very moment he returned he realized that Sandy Springs is the heart of all homes for turtles!

Builder Bob

By Lilli Bailey
Age 12. 7th Grade,
Dickerson Middle
School

The turtle Builder Bob is a special turtle. Builder Bob is special because he was created in memory of a very special man, Bob Johnson. This man was also my granddad. Actually we called him Captain Bob because he was the Captain of our hearts. Builder Bob started building houses in the late 1950's. He loved creating and building the finest quality homes. In fact, he always said he never built a home he wouldn't move into himself. If you look on the back of his shell you will see a map. This shows all the homes he built in and around Sandy Springs. He was proud to live in Sandy Springs. I like to visit him at the post office because he smiles and welcomes everyone coming in and out. If you knew Builder Bob like I knew Builder Bob, you would think he was special too.

Shelly Desiree

By Rachel McGovern
Age 8. 3rd Grade, Warren T. Jackson Elementary School

There once was a turtle named Shelly who loved to show off her lime green belly.

Beach, pool, or lake doesn't matter, she always looks great! With those nails and toes that sparkle through snow they should always be done for a party you know.

One day, oh no! What could be wrong? Shelly forgot to put her sunblock on. She fell asleep on turtle beach. The longer she slept the redder she got.

Poor Shelly, it hurt like the devil as her beauty green skin turned shades of yellow and brown. Her friends would tease her she thought and quickly hid in her boxshell.

Later Shelly got hungry.

She peeked out and to her surprise she saw balloons and candles and heard her friends saying its not what's on the outside, its what's on the inside that makes you sparkle!

Come party all night Shelly Desiree.

Write your own Town Turtle story about

Fred Asturtle

Lucky

By Jack Staples
Age 8. 2nd Grade, Holy Innocents' Episcopal School

Lucky, the cowboy turtle, lived a very poor life in a little desert sand dune. Lucky was almost killed by a rattlesnake, but thank goodness he dug down deep into the sand and escaped—that is how he got his name!

When Lucky grew up he had plenty of adventures. One time, Lucky was walking in the middle of the desert. It was about 5:50 in the afternoon when all of a sudden a sandstorm came up. Lucky got out safely because he hid in his shell, stuck out his little feet, dug a deep hole, and hid from the storm.

After that happened, Lucky decided to move somewhere safer, to a place where there were no sandstorms . . . Sandy Springs!

One day, Lucky's Sandy Springs neighbor went outside, took off his shell and began taking a bath. Lucky noticed a bandit turtle trying to steal the neighbor's shell. Lucky ran outside and threw his lasso around the shell and chased the bandit away.

The neighbor turtle and the other town turtles named him Sheriff and gave him a badge. Lucky's job is to keep Sandy Springs safe.

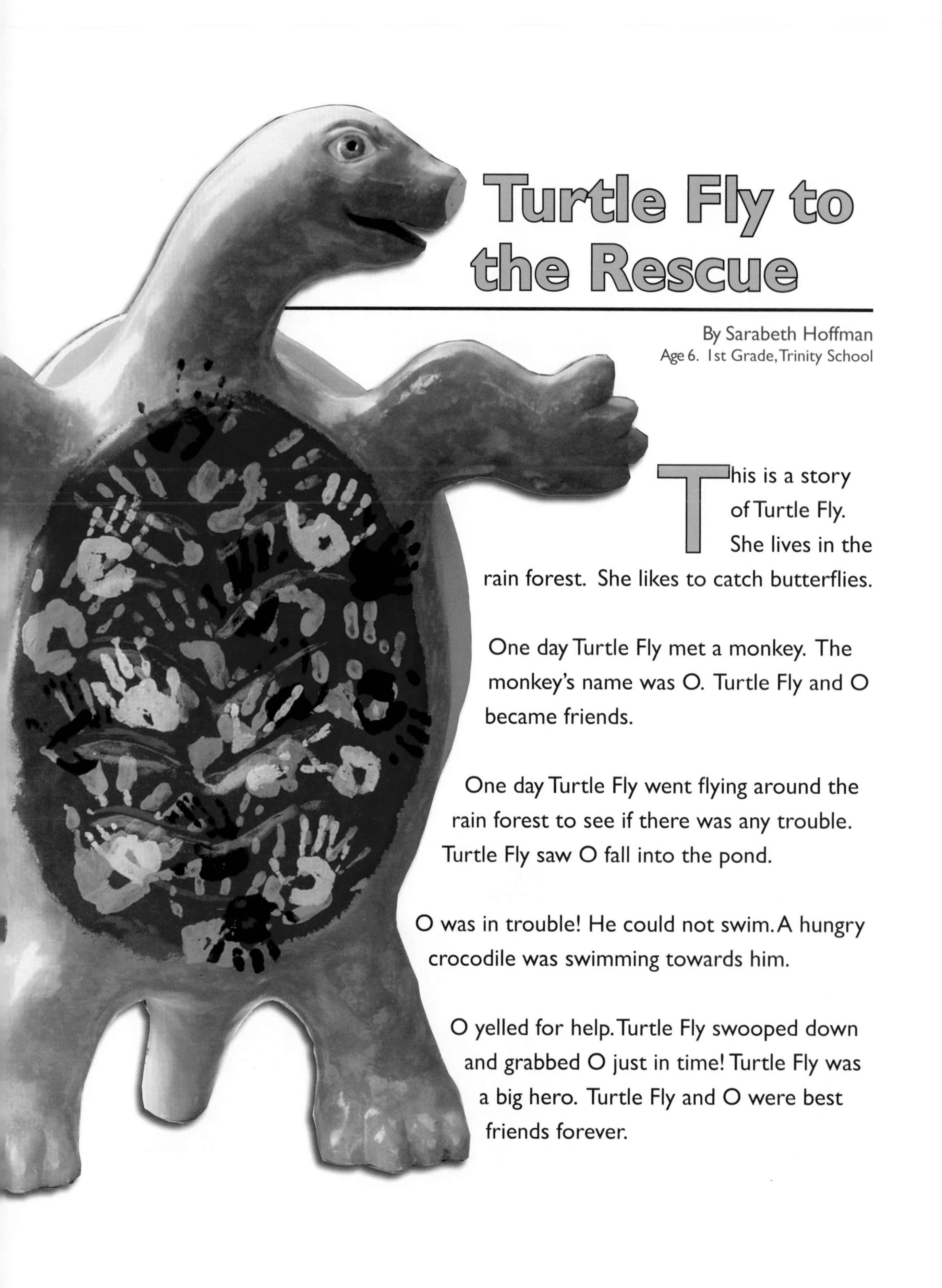

Turtle Fly to the Rescue

By Sarabeth Hoffman
Age 6. 1st Grade, Trinity School

This is a story of Turtle Fly. She lives in the rain forest. She likes to catch butterflies.

One day Turtle Fly met a monkey. The monkey's name was O. Turtle Fly and O became friends.

One day Turtle Fly went flying around the rain forest to see if there was any trouble. Turtle Fly saw O fall into the pond.

O was in trouble! He could not swim. A hungry crocodile was swimming towards him.

O yelled for help. Turtle Fly swooped down and grabbed O just in time! Turtle Fly was a big hero. Turtle Fly and O were best friends forever.

Window Box

By Sophia Petritz
Age 7. 1st Grade, Vanderlyn Elementary School

My favorite turtle is the window box turtle because she lives near the Chattahoochee River and my Grammy. The window box turtle likes to smell and pick flowers. She likes to swim with ducks, and she likes to wave to everyone.

I also like other turtles but I like this one the best.

I also think that she's magical. Maybe she goes out at night when no one is looking.

Perhaps she swims in the river. I don't know what she does, but I like her a lot.

Well its time for me to go, but I'll see you next time. Bye!

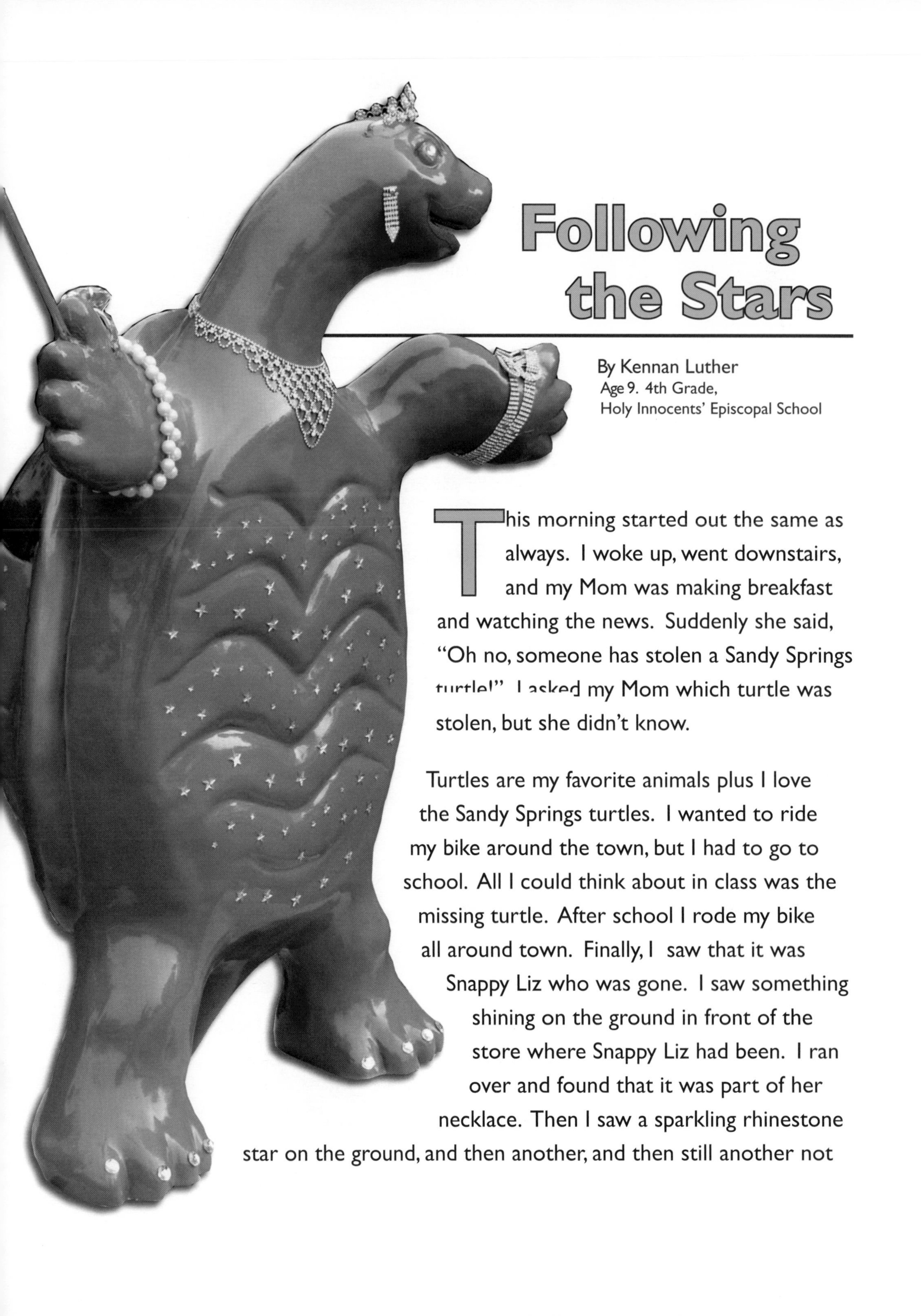

Following the Stars

By Kennan Luther
Age 9. 4th Grade,
Holy Innocents' Episcopal School

This morning started out the same as always. I woke up, went downstairs, and my Mom was making breakfast and watching the news. Suddenly she said, "Oh no, someone has stolen a Sandy Springs turtle!" I asked my Mom which turtle was stolen, but she didn't know.

Turtles are my favorite animals plus I love the Sandy Springs turtles. I wanted to ride my bike around the town, but I had to go to school. All I could think about in class was the missing turtle. After school I rode my bike all around town. Finally, I saw that it was Snappy Liz who was gone. I saw something shining on the ground in front of the store where Snappy Liz had been. I ran over and found that it was part of her necklace. Then I saw a sparkling rhinestone star on the ground, and then another, and then still another not too far away. I decided to follow this trail of sparkling rhinestone stars.

After a while, it seemed like I had been walking forever, and it was starting to get dark. I needed to go home.

Just as I was about to go back, I saw a huge ring in front of a house. When I knocked on the door it opened, so I went in. It was very dark inside. Something on the floor was shining. It was Snappy Liz!

She was all broken. I ran over to her and sat down, but I couldn't fix her broken parts. It was so late I finally fell asleep. When I woke up I couldn't believe it. Snappy Liz was fixed. Her stars were shining on her shell and I thought I saw a tear in her eye.

I was so happy I ran to get the owner. The next day Snappy Liz was back at her spot at the store. Every day I rode my bike to the store, and every day her smile seemed to get wider and wider.

Her stars must be magic!

A Plate Fit For the President

By Jorie Moran
Age 9. 3rd Grade, Trinity School

One day a customer ate at Slow Cookin'. This was where Turtle Soup worked. She was a wonderful cook.

When the customer was finished eating, she asked if Turtle Soup would be interested in entering a contest.

"Of course I would," Turtle Soup replied.

It was a contest to cook dinner for the President.

Turtle Soup was excited and

worried. What kind of dish do you cook for the President?

She thought of some of her favorite recipes: Nut Turtle Zucchini; White Chocolate Turtles (but those were too sweet); Turtle Pie (it had too many avocadoes); Café Latte Turtle Cake (but she was out of coffee); or Beef Turtles.

Then Tortoise Tenderloin came to mind.

She knew this would be the perfect plate for the President! … and it was!

When the President tasted Turtle Soup's Tortoise Tenderloin, he exclaimed, "This is Tremendous!"

The End

Fil-A-Gree

By Mallika Madhusudan
Age 9. 4th Grade,
The Westminster Schools

Cowering in the shadows was Fil-A-Gree, a plain, round turtle. "You ugly, miserable creature," Zenda the witch shrieked. "Do your work!"

Fil-A-Gree had been captured and forcefully enslaved by Zenda.

One day a huge, blue dragonfly with wings like delicate lace flew in the window. Swiftly,

Zenda cast a spell and the dragonfly froze in mid-air. She stuffed it in a cage.

The dragonfly whispered pleadingly to Fil-A-Gree, "Help me, help me please!"

Fil-A-Gree said, "Hush little friend. I'll set you free when the witch goes to sleep tonight."

Just before dawn, Fil-A-Gree released the dragonfly. The dragonfly turned into a fairy and set Fil-A-Gree free from the witch's spell.

As the sun's rays rose in the sky, Fil-A-Gree set out to enjoy her newfound freedom. She peered into a lake nearby and gasped in amazement. "My shell!" she cried in wonderment. "It's beautiful. It's like hardened lace!"

Tortoise and the Chair

By Emma Rose Spiegel
Age 8. 3rd Grade,
The Alfred and
Adele Davis
Academy

Once upon a time there lived a turtle. That turtle was not just any turtle. He was named Mr. Frank.

Mr. Frank was the best magician in the world. He could do card tricks and ball tricks.

But the best part was watching him do tricks that he invented.

After nineteen years he invented "chair in the air."

"Chair in the air" is when he makes chairs and then he makes them float in the air. Soon after "chair in the air" was invented he became very rich.

In 1832, Turtle, Georgia, was founded. Three years later Mr. Frank moved there. He met many turtles while living there and had lots of time to invent things.

In 1893, Mr. Frank changed his name to Benjamin Franklin. Soon after that, "chair in the air" became so popular, and his house was filled with so much money, that the air could not get through to him. So he put his money in all the banks he could find and he moved into a mansion.

Then he married Amelia Earhart and thogether they invented "plane in the air." It could fly! Five years later, Benjamin and Amelia had two kids named Abraham Lincoln and George Washington. The turtle family had so much fun together. But don't forget that this whole family started with a magician who invented "chair in the air."

The Turtle King

By Shaluma Reynolds
Age 6. 1st Grade,
Spalding Drive
Elementary School

A long, long, loooong time ago in a big, fat tin can lived an old and rather poor turtle. His name was Tiny Tortoise. He had no food and no water, and his wife, Ms. Flowers, never laid eggs.

Because these turtles lived far from the ocean, they never swam. Every day all they did was crawl in their shells and think about their future. As a matter of fact, thinking was the best thing they had.

One day Tiny Tortoise sat on his porch and looked up into the sky. As he did, a little pink blossom floated down from the sky and landed on the porch. It opened up and a fairy came out.

She waved her magic wand. Sparkles of light came out. Tiny Tortoise turned into Ivan the Terrapin King. He had a beautiful purple gown with fluffy white trim, golden crown, bracelets, and a gold chain with an eye in the middle.

"Wow!" he exclaimed, "MAGIC!" His wife laid 1,000,300 eggs. They danced all day, they had CHEESE Pizza and soda for a celebration, and they moved into a palace near the ocean so they could swim. And they lived happily ever after.

The End.

Julio Tortuga

By Chase Luther
Age 6. 1st Grade, Holy Innocents' Episcopal School

Julio Tortuga, the turtle, came to Atlanta to play with the Atlanta Braves. Someone told him to get on the Marta train and get off downtown. He got lost at lunchtime and was very hungry. He saw a sign that said, "Food at the Varsity," so he went in. He could not understand the way they were talking there. They said things like "naked dog, dog walkin', P. C." The only word he understood was "steak," but whenever anyone ordered "steak" they were served a hamburger. He also did not know what "Wha da ya have, wha da ya have, wha da ya have" meant.

He left the Varsity and walked down the street, and finally he saw the Braves' Stadium. He started running toward it. He got out on the field and started playing baseball. He had more hotdogs and got a tummy ache.

He walked down the street and found Centennial Olympic Park. He saw a big brown dog on the street. It had no collar. The dog followed him. He named his new buddy Truffles. They found the water fountains in the park and played in them with all the children.

Julio and Truffles walked on and saw a sign that said "Aquarium." They also saw a sign that said "No Dogs!" so Julio told Truffles to sit there. Truffles followed him into the building anyway.

Julio thought it was awesome to see fish swimming around everywhere. Truffles started barking, so Julio told him to get quiet.

Julio was surprised to see turtles almost like him swimming in the water. He felt like he was at home. He loved Atlanta.

Sparky

By Carson Staples
Age 6. 1st Grade,
Holy Innocents' Episcopal School

Sparky the fire turtle lives in a pond in Sandy Springs. He has five brothers and six sisters. His mom and dad live in a house near the pond as pets of the family who lives there.

In January of 2005 the family in the house had a loose brick in their fireplace, but they didn't know it. It was a cold day so they decided to start a fire in their fireplace.

The house caught on fire. Sparky told his brothers and sisters that he was going to get their mom and dad and the people who live in the house out. So Sparky sucked up as much water as he could from the pond and ran as fast as he could up the hill to the burning house. He was a little scared but brave enough to keep going.

Sparky crawled into the house through the cat door. He found his parents and told them to stay low to the ground. Sparky had the idea to rescue the family who lived in the house by carrying them out on the turtles' backs. Since there were three people in the house and three turtles in the house, the plan worked great!

Once they were safely outside, Sparky ran back down to the pond and got more water to spit on the fire. The fire truck from Station #2 came, and the firemen asked the family what happened. The family told the firemen about how brave Sparky was and how his quick thinking had saved their lives.

The firemen told Sparky he was a hero and asked him to come back to the fire station with them and to become the official fire turtle of Sandy Springs!

Sparky Saves the Day

By Kallie Asher, age 6; Jonathan Barnette, age 7; Frankie Chapman, age 6; Zachary Draper, age 6; Chastity Grimes, age 6; Sarah Kern, age 6; Sahil Kirpalani, age 6; Gaby Pascual, age 6; & Suzannah Raney, age 6
Mrs. Omiencinski's 1st Grade class at the Atlanta Speech School.

Sparky is a fireman in Sandy Springs. He lives at the fire station.
One Friday morning, Sparky got up. He ate pancakes and cereal.
Then the fire bell rang. There was a fire.
Sparky got in his fire truck.
He drove to the fire.
Sparky took out the fire hose. He aimed it at the fire.
A mom and baby were trapped in the house.
Sparky climbed up the ladder to the window.
Sparky carried the mom and baby on his shell.
He took them outside.
He put a blanket around them.
Sparky the fireman put out the fire. He drove back to the fire station.
Sparky washed off the fire truck. He was happy he had saved another family.

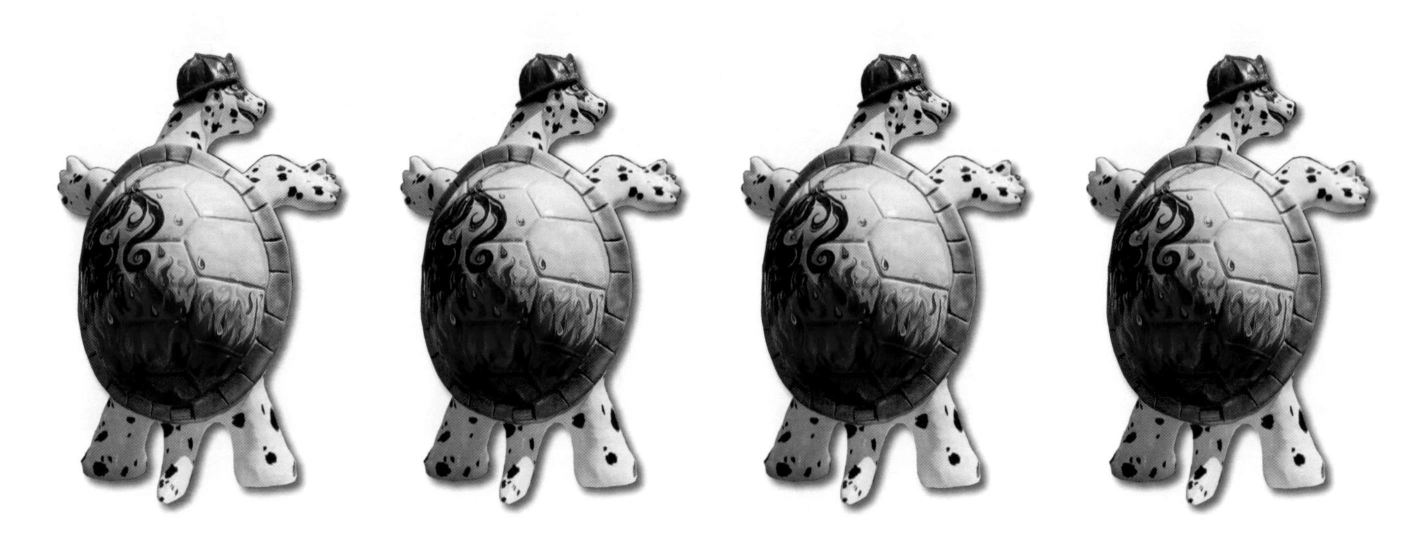

Travel Turtle's Trips

By Alice Ann Lever
Age 7. 2nd Grade,
Woodland Elementary Charter School

I'm going to tell you about Travel Turtle's trips.

Well, Bug World was pretty annoying for Travel Turtle. There were so many bugs!

When he visited the beach he went fishing every day. He loves fishing!

In Drama Land he got to be in a play. When he came home for a break, we went swimming together.

Then he went to the jungle and there he learned to speak to the lions—and that's all I know about.

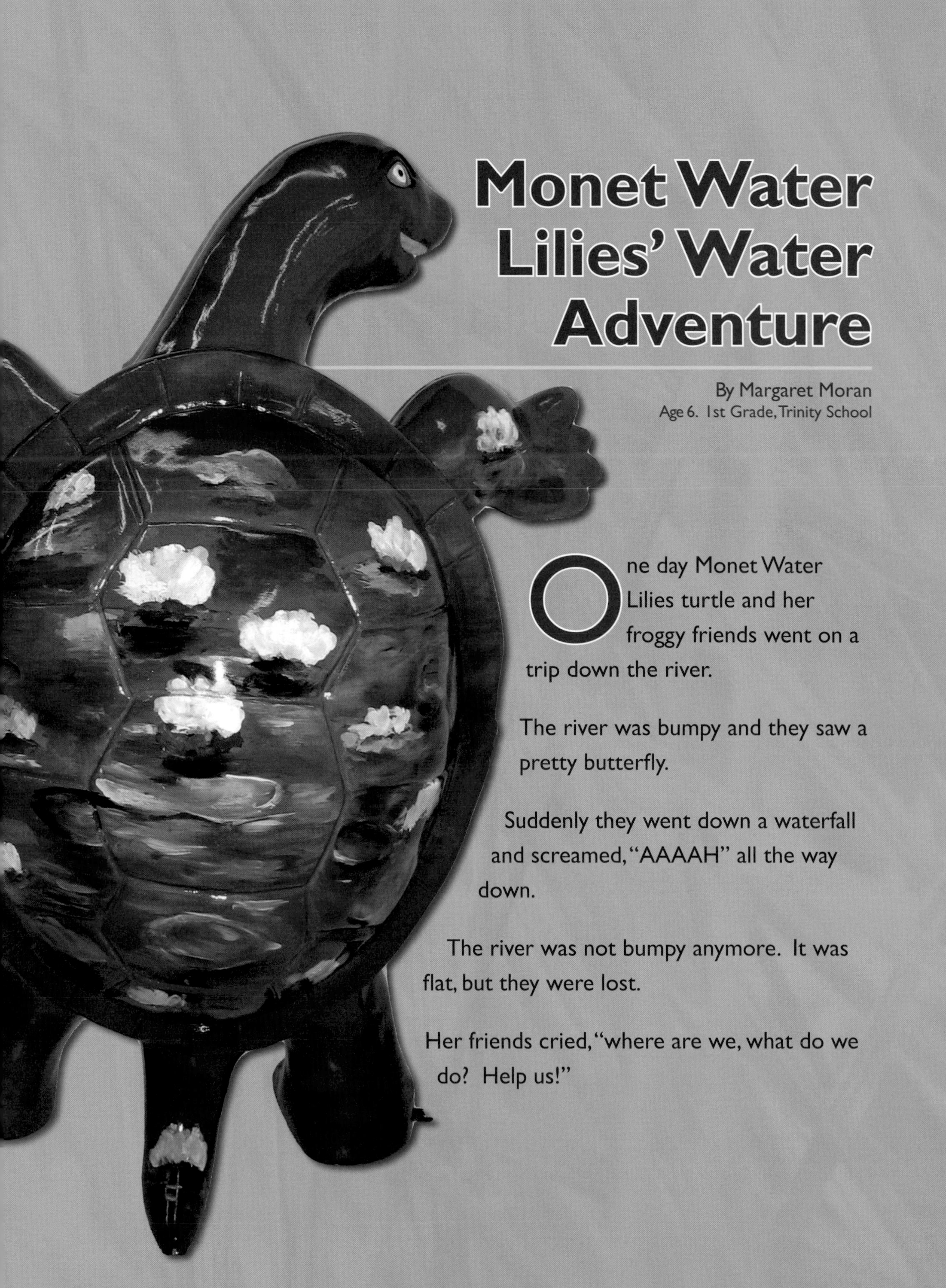

Monet Water Lilies' Water Adventure

By Margaret Moran
Age 6. 1st Grade, Trinity School

One day Monet Water Lilies turtle and her froggy friends went on a trip down the river.

The river was bumpy and they saw a pretty butterfly.

Suddenly they went down a waterfall and screamed, "AAAAH" all the way down.

The river was not bumpy anymore. It was flat, but they were lost.

Her friends cried, "where are we, what do we do? Help us!"

Monet Water Lilies thought and thought.

She thought she should help them so she said, "climb on my back!" So they did.

Monet Water Lilies swam and saw a fish. She asked, "How do we get home?" The fish said, " Where do you live?"

Monet Water Lilies told the fish. He said, "That is easy. Swim down stream, go left at the fork! That will take you home!"

So she did and they all made it home safe.

Stick Your Neck Out Turtle

By Faith MacDonald
Age 8. 3rd Grade,
Woodland Elementary Charter School

Once upon a time in a far away land was the small town of Turtleville. In this small town lived George Turtleton.

You see these weren't just any old turtles, no siree they weren't. They were magical turtles that could stand on their hind legs and walk. All of them, that is, except for George who had to crawl on four feet.

All the other kids laughed and called him names.

One night while George was sleeping his parents were taken away by mad scientists. That same night all the other adults in Turtleville also were kidnapped. When George woke up he found his parents were gone. On the way to school he saw that all the other kids were without parents too.

Because of this, they were too worried to tease him.

On his way home from school he fell into a hole—or so he thought. As he looked closer he saw it was not a hole but a footprint—and there were more footprints going out of the village toward the hills. He went back to tell the other kids about his discovery. While on his way he decided he would follow the enormous footprints. After explaining his plan to all the other kids, George set off following the footprints.

So he did just that. Along the way he met a fish, a bear (a friendly one at that), and a friendly fox named Foxy.

Then as he was walking, suddenly right before him was a pit of flames. He could either walk in and die or turn back toward home.

Just then a bird flew overhead and landed right in front of him. To his surprise it was the Bird of Kindenss. The Bird of Kindness was the pet of Mother Nature. She was the one who watched over all of nature.

The the bird spoke and said, "May I be of service, George?"

Puzzled, George said, "How do you know my name?"

"I know because I am the Bird of Kindness. I need to know everybody's name," she said.

"Now that that's settled, do you need my help or not?" the bird asked.

George answered very quickly. "Yes, I do need your help. I need to get across the pit of fire. Can you fly me over?"

"Why, of course I can," she said. "In fact, why don't I take you all the way to your destination?" she asked.

"That would be great," said George. "Just follow those footprints. O.K.?"

So the Bird of Kindness let George on her back and took off and followed the footprints to a huge wall. There she said, "This is as far as I go."

"O.K.," said George. So the Bird of Kindness let him off her back. Then George attempted to climb the wall. It took some effort, but finally he got to the other side and to the entrance of the mad scientists' lab. George climbed under the door and past all sorts of traps. Finally he got to a table where the scientists were working.

Then he saw a cage on the floor. It was filled with the adults from Turtleville. George crawled and let them out. He told them to crawl. They did as he said and crawled out of the lab, over the wall, and onto the Bird of Kindness' back for their ride to Turtleville. When everyone was back home safe and sound, no one called George any names anymore because he was a hero.

Write your own Town Turtle story about

Miss Sandi
The Tapping Turtlette

Hope the Box Turtle

By Rachel Hamilton
Age 9. 3rd Grade, Holy Spirit Preparatory School.

Once there was a turtle named Hope. She was sent from the sky to a special place on earth called Sandy Springs. She was unique because she was the only box turtle in the world who had a body that looked like the sky and a shell with pretty rainbow colors.

When she arrived on earth, she met two other turtles.

"Hey you! You look strange," yelled one.

"Yeah, too different!" agreed the other.

But Hope didn't care. "Thanks!" she exclaimed sweetly.

The others were confused.

Usually, if they teased someone because of how they looked, it made them run home weeping. They were surprised to see how easy-going she was.

"Bye," they mumbled. "Goodbye!" Hope called. "Have a wonderful day!"

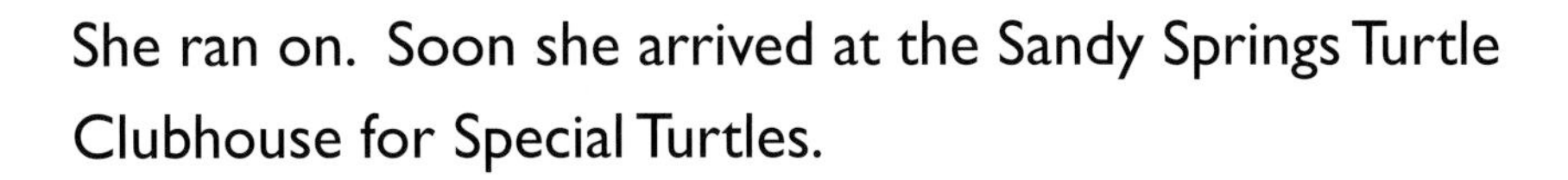

She ran on. Soon she arrived at the Sandy Springs Turtle Clubhouse for Special Turtles.

"Hello! welcome! My name is Sandy," one turtle introduced herself. "You must be Hope."

"Yes I am," replied Hope.

"We're so happy you're here! Hey, why don't you take a look around? You can meet the other 72 turtles. They're really nice, like you."

"Oh you're nice too."

"O.K. I'll take a look around."

Hope was happy to see a room full of colorful, unique, special turtles just like her.

One day Sandy announced that soon after all of the turtles had became very used to being away from home, she would send each of them on a special mission.

Weeks passed. Finally the day arrived.

A turtle named Sparky was sent to the Fire Department, not only because he was black and white like a dalmation, but because he had excellent fireman skills.

Mark Trail, another turtle, was sent to a park to help hikers find their way.

Every turtle had a wonderful job—especially Hope! She was sent to a hospital to fill the sick people's hearts with joy and happiness. She was very good at that. She had received the right job.

All the sick people at the hospital just looked at Hope, and she made them feel a little better, more joyful, and happier. When friends or family came to visit the sick people, she gave them hope that their friend or family member would feel better.

Just visit Hope whenever you need to. Many people know about her great success. While she is not at the hospital anymore, a statue of her stands there now. So visit her. Many people have seen her beauty and one day you will too!

Write your own Town Turtle story about

Doctor Turtle

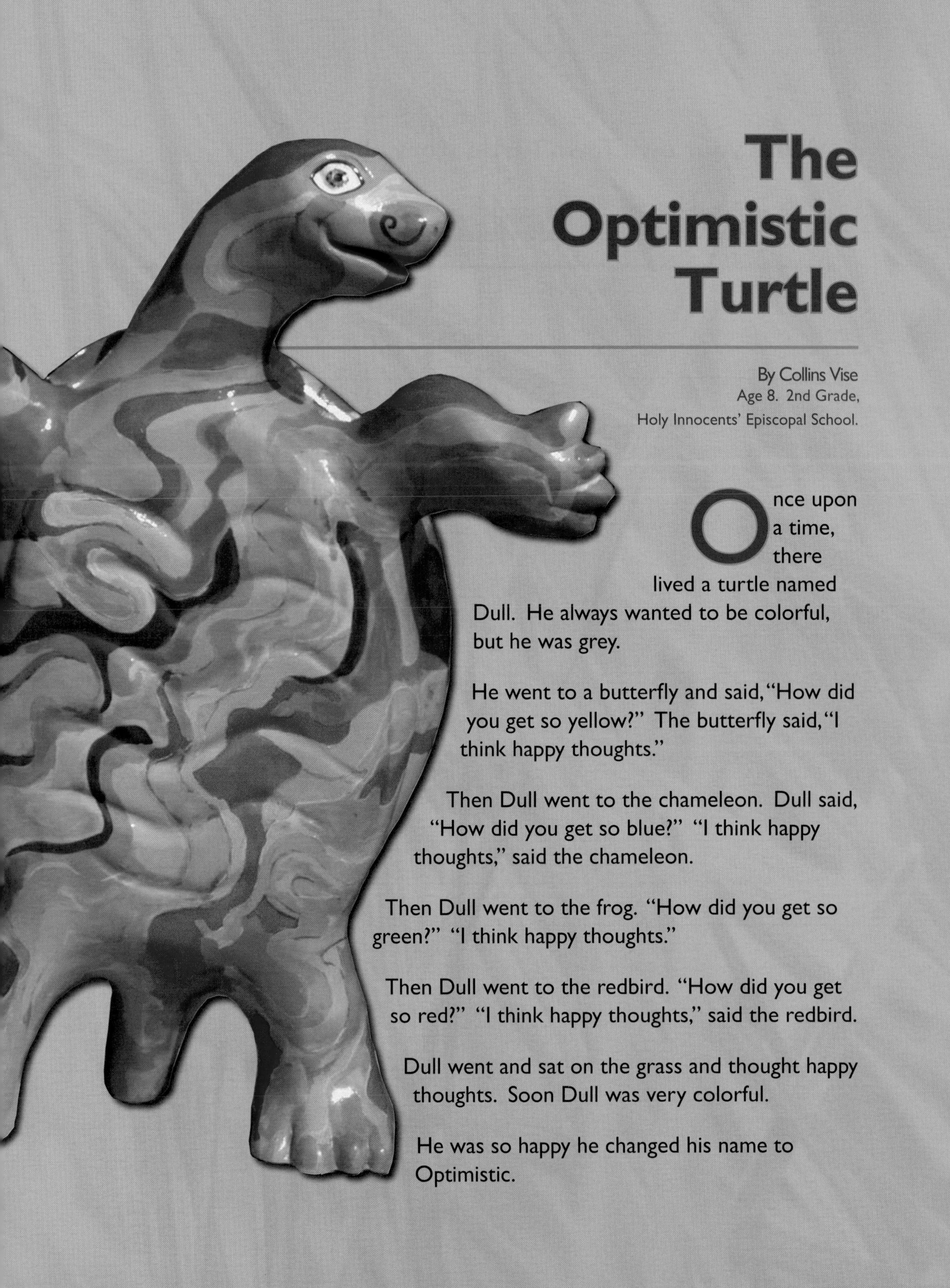

The Optimistic Turtle

By Collins Vise
Age 8. 2nd Grade,
Holy Innocents' Episcopal School.

Once upon a time, there lived a turtle named Dull. He always wanted to be colorful, but he was grey.

He went to a butterfly and said, "How did you get so yellow?" The butterfly said, "I think happy thoughts."

Then Dull went to the chameleon. Dull said, "How did you get so blue?" "I think happy thoughts," said the chameleon.

Then Dull went to the frog. "How did you get so green?" "I think happy thoughts."

Then Dull went to the redbird. "How did you get so red?" "I think happy thoughts," said the redbird.

Dull went and sat on the grass and thought happy thoughts. Soon Dull was very colorful.

He was so happy he changed his name to Optimistic.

Star the Spangled Turtle

By Julia Marie Bond
Age 7. 1st Grade, Trinity School.

When I was walking home from school I saw a letter in the mail. It was from one of the Sandy Springs Turtles. Star the Spangled Turtle was inviting me to his Birthday! On the big day I was excited! Just then, Chance (Chance is my next door neighbor's dog) ran toward him.

I had to save the turtle!

I ran, scooped Star the Spangled Turtle up and placed him in a tree. Then I grabbed Chance's collar and dragged her out of the yard.

Tuga the Turtle

By Liam Collins
Age 8. 2nd Grade,
Holy Innocents' Episcopal School

Once upon a time there was a turtle named Tuga.

Tuga didn't have any friends because all the other turtles made fun of the way he looked. He looked like a football on his dome shell, and he was red on his front shell.

One day in school, Tuga was opening his locker when he heard a clapping sound. He moved toward the sound. Finally he came to the auditorium. The Georgia Bulldog coach was making an announcement. He was calling out the names for the

Bulldogs team. He said there was a special leading turtle and that turtle was Tuga! Then, after school Tuga went to a game. It was his first game and he was excited.

The game started. After three quarters, it was the fourth quarter. The quarterback passed the ball and Tuga started running. He came to the end zone. Touchdown!!!

After the game, Tuga had many new friends because he was the star of the Georgia Bulldogs.

Road Warrior

By Andy Acosta
Age 12. 7th Grade, Peachtree Charter Middle School

Long ago there lived a green large turtle named Jimmy Treaty. He was 12 years old. He was always depressed with school, home, and everthing. One day, after failing the biggest test ever, The Turtle FIQ, he decided to run away to see his home state, Georgia.

"On the road of life I'll fly," said Jimmy.

Jimmy had never really got to know his state very well, so he used his life's savings, caught a bus, and away he went. Jimmy decided to draw a map on himself of everywhere he went. After several months, he had visited so many places that his body had become a map of Georgia.

From malls to halls, from Stone Mountain to Centennial Park fountains, from DeKalb to Gwinnett and Cumming, and from Six Flags to White Water he went. Every time he went somewhere he added to the map he drew on himself.

After he finished exploring across the state of Georgia, Jimmy went back close to his own town. He stood under the Interstate 285-East highway bridge. From there he saw people, dogs, cats, lizards, aliens, and even the president. But what caught Jimmy's attention was a family. He saw them together as one and that made him miss his own family.

Jimmy ran home and explained to his worried mom what had happened. Days later she forgave him. When Jimmy went back to school, his new name was Map Warrior.

Map Warrior had learned that a family should stick together. They would help him through his moments of despair. He should never give up on himself.

During his travels, he had also discovered his home state. But Jimmy forgot one thing. Permanent marker does not come off of Turtles!

So, the next time you need to find a place, call Jimmy!

By William Howard Mavity II
Age 11. 5th Grade,
Holy Innocents' Episcopal School

I huddled in a dark space, rocking in the rhythm of waves.

I could recall being inside the Louvre. I could remember hearing a voice say, "He's perfect! I'll take him." Another voice said, "It's a museum, not a store."

We'll see," she said. I must have fallen asleep because this shack was not the Louvre.

Suddenly voices started yelling. I heard a loud CRACK! as my crate started sliding. My crate went overboard, filling

with water. This
was the end.
Suddenly my
crate hit land,
dumping me out.

Then I saw a lady, who said,
"You're the cutest thing!"
The lady helped me up
and informed me that
I was on Madagascar
where a colony of wild
turtles lived.

She explained that the
turtles had become violent.

"They need a leader," she
said. "How about you?"

I agreed, and soon found
myself sitting on a throne,
watching over everyone.

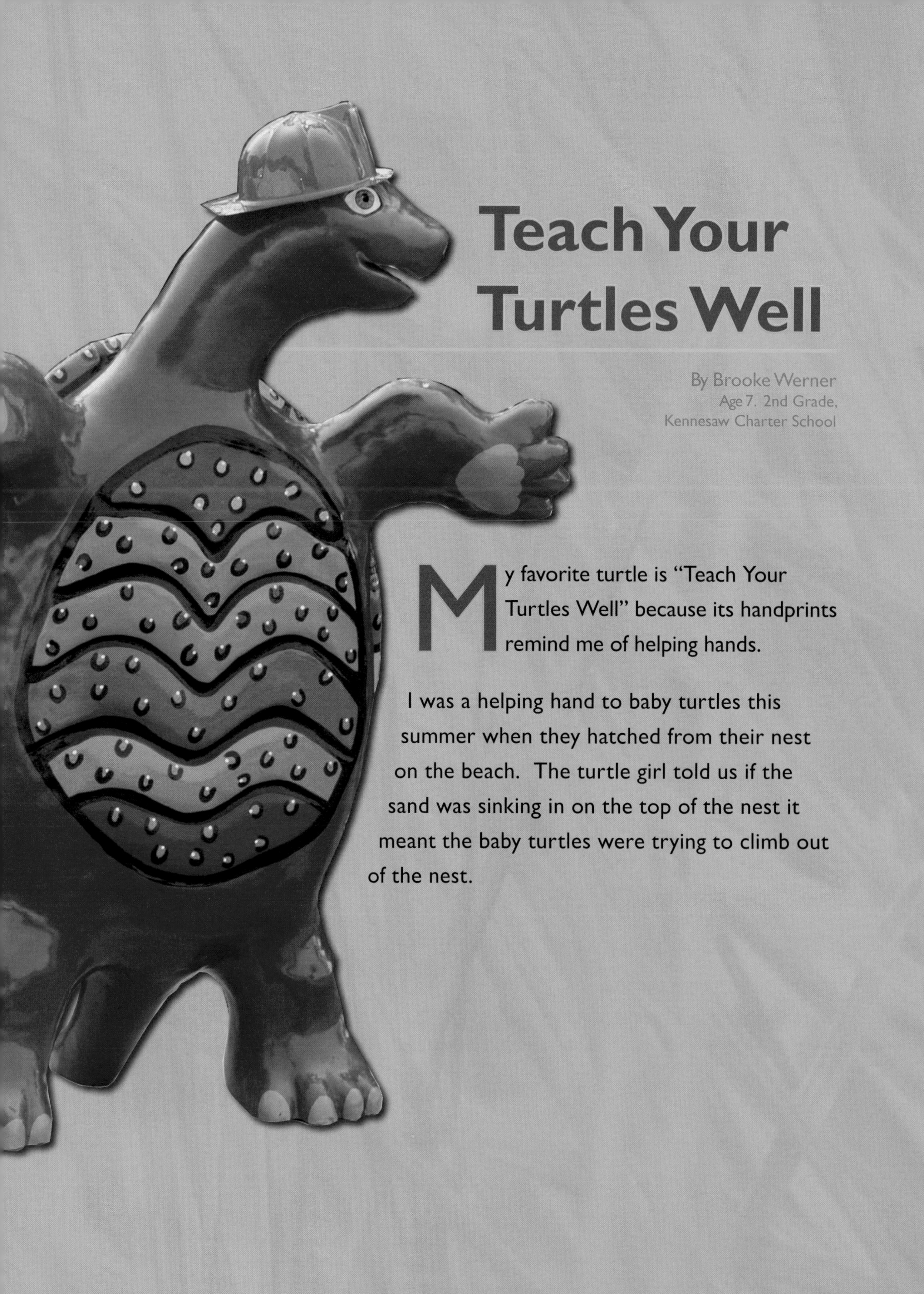

Teach Your Turtles Well

By Brooke Werner
Age 7. 2nd Grade,
Kennesaw Charter School

My favorite turtle is "Teach Your Turtles Well" because its handprints remind me of helping hands.

I was a helping hand to baby turtles this summer when they hatched from their nest on the beach. The turtle girl told us if the sand was sinking in on the top of the nest it meant the baby turtles were trying to climb out of the nest.

We stood close and saw the first turtle crawl out of the sand. Then bunches and bunches of baby turtles came up out of the sand and hurried down to the water.

Everyone stood close to make sure that raccoons and ghost crabs didn't eat the baby turtles. We saw the baby turtles go into the ocean. The turtle girls said they would swim for many years until they got old enough to come back to Little Cumberland Island to lay their own eggs.

Mark Trail True Turtle

By Jack Portman
Age 6. 1st Grade,
Simpson Elementary School

I was looking at the Mark Trail True Turtle from the Turtle Parade. Right before my eyes he became alive! He dropped to the ground. I ran around looking for him. Then I found him hiding in the bushes. He talked to me.

He said, "What happened?" I said, "You became alive!"

He asked who I was. I said, "I am Jack."

He asked, "Can you bring me back to the pond?" I said, "Yes."

I asked him how far away it was and he said, "over there." I brought him back to his pond.

I hope you have a good time in there," I said to him and he swam off. I watched him until he disappeared.

I hurried back to my parents.

I stopped in my tracks.

All the turtles were alive! I took them all back to their home in the pond.

They lived happily ever after.

Write your own Town Turtle story about

Fen

Hero

By Austin Britton-Davis
Age 10. 5th Grade,
Holy Innocents' Episcopal School

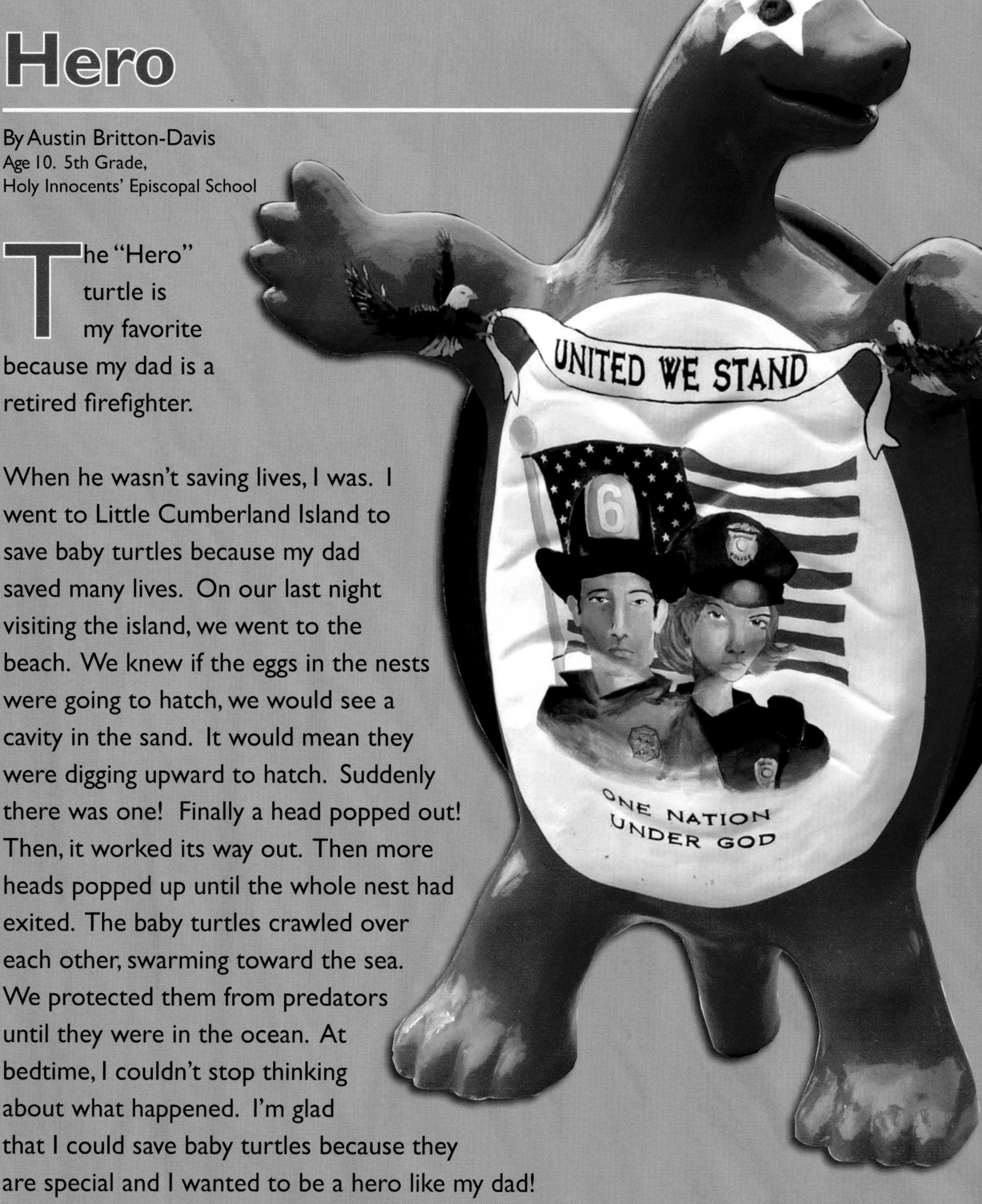

The "Hero" turtle is my favorite because my dad is a retired firefighter.

When he wasn't saving lives, I was. I went to Little Cumberland Island to save baby turtles because my dad saved many lives. On our last night visiting the island, we went to the beach. We knew if the eggs in the nests were going to hatch, we would see a cavity in the sand. It would mean they were digging upward to hatch. Suddenly there was one! Finally a head popped out! Then, it worked its way out. Then more heads popped up until the whole nest had exited. The baby turtles crawled over each other, swarming toward the sea. We protected them from predators until they were in the ocean. At bedtime, I couldn't stop thinking about what happened. I'm glad that I could save baby turtles because they are special and I wanted to be a hero like my dad!

A Turtle for Her Birthday

By Annika Garbers
Age 7. 3rd Grade, Calvert School
(homeschool)

Once upon a time there was a family. They had a little baby girl. Her first word was "turtle."

All the little girl wanted for each birthday, Christmas—all the time—was the same thing: turtles!

One day, her big sister said, "Look Mom, it's a brochure on the Town Turtles of Sandy Springs. We could do that for Ariana on her birthday!"

"Good idea," said her mom.

So the family went on a "turtle hunt." They took pictures of the kids with the turtles. They did that for two days. They had lots of fun.

Ariana's favorite turtle was Georgia O'Turtle, which she called "Flower Turtle."

Secretly, the mom, dad, Will, and Annika made a book with the pictures of the turtles. Annika wrote a story about the "turtle hunt" and Georgia O'Turtle for the book.

They gave it to Ariana for her birthday. She said, "Now this really is the best present ever!"

Slow-down Town Turtle

By Andee Poulos
Age 9. 3rd Grade,
Holy Innocents' Episcopal School

This story is about Slow-dow Town Turtle. Slow-down is the turtle that represents Rivershore Estates. I live in Rivershore Estates so I get to see him a lot. When some high school kids were stealing Town Turtles, they stole Slow-down! When the high school kids who stole the turtles were found, they were arrested. A lot of the stolen turtles were found in a river and one in a forest. Slow-down got his head cut off! After he was found, people did something to put his head back on the body. Then they put a collar on his neck to hide where his head had been cut off. After his head was fixed, he came back to Rivershore Estates and stayed for a long time. Then he went to the Town Turtles auction. There he was sold to someone who bid the most money for him. Slow-down was very brave and I am very proud of him.

The Beautiful American Turtle

By Elizabeth Ann White
Age 6. Home School

"Daddy, how did America get started?"

"Well, the Pilgrims came to America and started America."

"What are the colors of America?"

"Red, White, and Blue."

"Daddy, could I paint my shell red and white, and my body blue?"

"Little Turtle, you are my star."

"Yes Daddy, and I am an American."

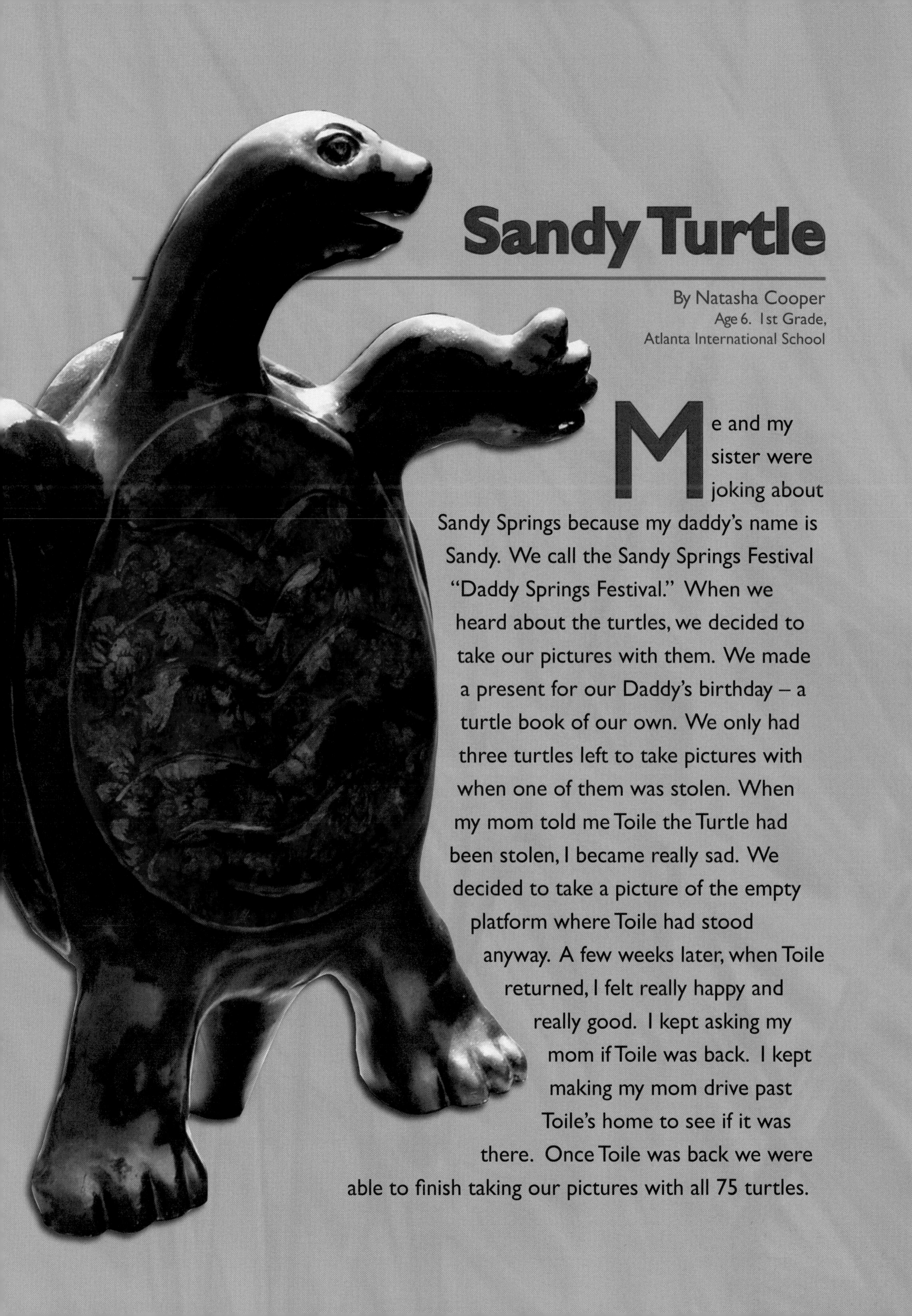

Sandy Turtle

By Natasha Cooper
Age 6. 1st Grade,
Atlanta International School

Me and my sister were joking about Sandy Springs because my daddy's name is Sandy. We call the Sandy Springs Festival "Daddy Springs Festival." When we heard about the turtles, we decided to take our pictures with them. We made a present for our Daddy's birthday – a turtle book of our own. We only had three turtles left to take pictures with when one of them was stolen. When my mom told me Toile the Turtle had been stolen, I became really sad. We decided to take a picture of the empty platform where Toile had stood anyway. A few weeks later, when Toile returned, I felt really happy and really good. I kept asking my mom if Toile was back. I kept making my mom drive past Toile's home to see if it was there. Once Toile was back we were able to finish taking our pictures with all 75 turtles.

Princess

By Lauren Tsai
Age 11. 6th Grade, Holcomb Bridge Middle School

A four-legged critter
Wandering in the sand,
Looked for a princess
From a faraway land,
Longing to see her beauty
And her lovely shell,
Craving to hear her voice
Sweet as a tinkling bell.

Wandering day and night,
Hoping to glimpse of her
A sight.

Days flew by
While searching for the princess
From a faraway land.

Suddenly the sky opened,
God reached down a helping hand.
He lifted the turtle
Out of the sand.

Soon he saw her shining face,
That gorgeous shell
Decorated with lace.
He fell in love
Head over heels.
His eyes were round as wheels!

Soon another lover came.
They dueled
For the Princess of Suriname.

But that four-legged critter,
The one from Brazil,
Had the will.
With all his might,
He gathered his strength
And put up a fight!

He won!
Married the princess,
Had a big family,
And lived together quite happily.

Write your own Town Turtle story about

What's Your Hurry?

Write your own Town Turtle story about

Percy the Perservering Turtle

Did You Know That ... ?

Turtles have been around for 200,000,000 years.

Turtles lived when the dinosaurs roamed the earth.

Turtles do not have teeth.

Turtles come from eggs and after the eggs are laid, the mother never sees them again.

Turtles cannot live in arctic climates.

Turtles' bony parts are mostly on the outside of their body.

Turtles that lived millions of years ago in the ocean where South Dakota is today, grew to be 12 feet long.

Turtles, called box turtles, can live for more than 100 years. The box turtle can close all the openings of its shell so that is why it is called the box turtle.

Turtles have 220 species and 44 live in the United States.

Who is the real Jack Elrod?

Jack Elrod designed "Sandy" the Town Turtle figure.

Jack Elrod writes and illustrates the syndicated Mark Trail Nature strip.

Mark Trail is seen by 23 million people around the world each week.

Jack Elrod created the illustration on the facing page especially for the Town Turtles of Sandy Springs project.

Jack Elrod and his wife live in Sandy Springs.

Jack Elrod is the artist of the Mark Trail True Turtle in this book.

Acknowledgements

I am grateful to Sharon Corin, the children's librarian in the Sandy Springs Public Library, for selecting the stories included in this book from the hundreds of tales children wrote and submitted.

I also want to thank my wife, Harriet, together with Jan Collins, Ingrid Brunt, and Courtenay Collins for their help in creating this book. Thanks also to Karen Latta of Henderson-Shapiro for her assistance. Esther Patrick of Atlanta, Georgia, designed the book. Her advice–given graciously and with good humor–made this book better.

Finally, I want to thank David Yntema and Hardin Publishing for making it all happen.

Martin Moran, M.D.
Sandy Springs, Georgia
November, 2005

INDEX OF ARTISTS AND SPONSORS:

HOMER
Sponsor: Harry Norman Realtors
Artist: Shirley Sharp
DESIREE
Sponsor: Bernadine and Jean-Paul Richard
Artist: Rob Deloach
LUCKY
Sponsor: The UPS Store Sandy Springs
Artist: Christopher Hauck
BUILDER BOB
Sponsor: Bob Johnson Development Company
Artist: Magnolia Garden Club & Emily Johnson
SNAPPY LIZ
Sponsor: Knox Jewelers
Artist: Eddie Knox
WINDOW BOX TURTLE
Sponsor: Mimms Enterprises
Artist: Sarah Watkins
TURTLE SOUP—TRIBUTE TO JULIA CHILD
Sponsor: Publix Supermarket
Artist: Rena Sartain
TURTLE FLY
Sponsor: Jeanine Hurt Lewis
Artists: Holy Innocents' Episcopal School Students
TURTLE FIL-A-GREE
Sponsor: Mimms Enterprises
Artist: Mary Davis
THE TORTOISE AND THE CHAIR
Sponsor: Chair in the Air Designs
Artist: Tammie Kosack
IVAN THE TERRAPIN
Sponsor: Mimms Enterprises
Artist: Cherry Larkin
TRAVEL TURTLE
Sponsor: Equinox Group
Artist: Jeanne Colin
JULIO TORTUGA
Sponsor: Devin Properties, Inc.
Artist: David Carlton
SPARKY
Sponsor: R.J. Griffin & Company
Artist: Valerie Tschappat Thompson
MONET WATER LILIES
Sponsor: Dan and Beka Whigham
Artist: Berthe Mobasser
MRSTICKYOURNECKOUTFOR
SANDYSPRINGS
Sponsor: Kroger (Sandy Springs)
Artist: John Feight
HOPE
Sponsor: Saint Joseph's Hospital
Artist: Leslye Wilkins
BOTTISHELLI
Sponsor: Tom & Linda Morris
Artist: Wendy Jackson
ROAD WARRIOR
Sponsor: Mori Luggage & Gifts
Artist: Clarice Elder
TUGA
Sponsor: Mr and Mrs. V. Andrew Gill
Artist: Valerie Tschappat Thompson
"STAR" THE SPANGLED TURTLE
Sponsor: Jenny Pruitt & Associates, Realtors
Artist: Emily Juckett
THE OPTIMISTIC TURTLE
Sponsor: Cardsmart
Artist: Barbara Ladin Fisher
TEACH YOUR TURTLES WELL
Sponsor: Evelyn P. Barken
Artist: Kristy McCarthy
MARK TRAIL TRUE TURTLE
Sponsor: Burr & Forman LLC
Artist: Jack Elrod
HERO
Sponsor: Newman-Berbaum Foundation
Artists: Ashley Newman, Mark Elwood, Beth Deery
GEORGIA O'TURTLE
Sponsor: Fidelity Bank
Artist: Laura Shainker
SLOW DOWN TOWN TURTLE
Sponsor: Rivershore Estates Neighborhood
Artist: Anke Schofield
THE BEAUTIFUL AMERICAN TURTLE
Sponsor: Commissioner Tom Lowe
Artist: Hank Schwab
TOILE THE TURTLE
Sponsor: The John & Nancy Bell Family Foundation
Artist: Jennifer Gibbs
"MISS SANDY" THE TAPPING TURTLETTE
Sponsor: Kilim Collection (Bennet Street) Don and Grace Sentell
Artist: Ann Sample
PERCY THE PERSERVERING TURTLE
Sponsor: Coldwell Banker Residential Brokerage
Artist: Kathryn Denson
FRED ASTURTLE SHALL WE DANCE
Sponsor: Professional Gown Preservation
Artist: Mary Davis
WHAT'S YOUR HURRY?
Sponsor: Spring Landing Partners, LLC
Artist: Beth Stormont
FEN
Sponsor: The Billi Marcus Foundation
Artist: Linda Leeger Stokes
DOCTOR TURTLE
Sponsor: Northside Hospital
Artist: Jeanne Colin